RUPERT
FUN

Express Books

Published by Express Newspapers plc, 121 Fleet St., London, EC4P 4JT
Printed by Purnell Book Production Ltd., Paulton, Bristol, England.

CONTENTS

© 1988 Express Newspapers, 121 Fleet Street, London, EC4P 4JT

Stories as adapted by OBERON BV, Holland, from the original works of the late Alfred Bestall, M.B.E., with translations by Marinet Parker and editing by James Henderson. Cover and new illustrations by John Harrold.

RUPERT

and the

LITTLE MEN

Telling how a cap led Rupert into another adventure and how he rescued a band of little men.

Exploring the hills near his Nutwood home, Rupert makes a discovery...

Gosh, it's a castle! I haven't noticed that before!

I've always wanted to have a look inside a castle.

But as he hurries towards the castle he hears a familiar voice.

Hello Rupert!

Algy! What are you doing here?

Just taking a walk. But look what I've found!

What a strange hat!

I've no idea who it belongs to. I've seen no one.

Listen! There is somebody crying!

It's a little man, and look at his belt!

I say, it's just like the hat I found!

HELP!

No, please don't hurt me!

We won't hurt you! Is this your hat?

How the little man comes to be here is a strange tale. His friends have all been captured by a giant. Only he has escaped.

Come along, and I'll show you where they are.

18

4

5

Silently Rupert explores the castle. All the rooms are empty. Suddenly...

That came from the dungeons!

HELP!

At last! Oh please untie me, little bear!

Of course, I shall! Who are you?

I'm Greybeard the little men's leader! The giant says I'm too old to dig.

Don't worry, I've found the treasure...

...your friends are digging in the wrong place!

By the time Rupert has freed Greybeard he has thought of a plan that may free the little men.

I've an idea! Shut all the doors and windows and bolt them!

As soon as that's done, Rupert says he'll send Algy up.

I want Algy and you to go onto the battlements and shout to attract the giant's attention!

Just as you say!

...that's my plan. So up you go, Algy!

Right. But you be careful.

I just hope this will work!

YAH! BOO! STUPID OLD GIANT!

Hey! What's all this?

7

Huffing and puffing with rage, the giant lumbers up to the castle entrance.

He's fallen for it!

In here! We'll be safe in this crevice!

What luck, Algy finding this hammer. Let's get these chains off!

Very soon they are free and heading for the treasure.

There it is! The King's treasure you were digging for!

Wonderful, Rupert!

We still have to get out of here. So let's find Greybeard!

Oh, aren't we pleased to see you!

Now let's have a look at what that giant's up to!

HEY THERE! I'M WARNING YOU!

Good! He's still outside!

OPEN THAT DOOR NOW! or I'll get a 'tree and BREAK it down!

But Rupert isn't going to open the door— at least, not yet!

First, we're going to move the treasure. Come on!

22

8

E veryone joins in moving the gold to where the giant can't reach it.

That's it! Now the gold will be safe.

Let's hope he falls for it!

I'll hide you under this cloth. Don't stir when we come in.

Good luck, Youngster!

Right, here goes!

D ismally, Rupert tells the giant they have found the gold but are giving in.

Very wise! Now, show me where the gold is and maybe I won't make mincemeat of you all.

Up this way first, Sir.

This better be true or there'll be trouble!

Down there, Sir, at the bottom of the hole!

I'll take a look, and if you're lying.....!

O ut of the box pops Greybeard as the giant disappears.

23

9

UP comes the rope and it's up to him how he finds his way up again!

Down the castle rock Rupert dashes to tell the others the good news.

You can come out now, and bring the gold! We've won!

Tomorrow morning we take the treasure to our young King!

But first we have a party! In honour of Rupert and Algy!

Long live our young friends!

But for them we'd still be the giant's slaves!

Only the thought that their parents might be worried make the pals leave the party at last.

Gosh! It seems an awfully long way back to Nutwood!

Well, the sooner we start the better.

Wasn't it nice of the little men to give us a hat!

24

Hi, Daddy, I'm back!

Wait until you hear what happened to Algy and me!

Very soon Mr. and Mrs. Bear are chuckling at the pals in the little men hats.

...so the giant's really in a bit of a hole!

Good for you! Now we'd better let Algy's parent's know he's all right.

THE GIANT'S FOOTPRINTS GAME

This game is played on the footprints in the two ovals. First copy the two green footprints on thin card so that they can be cut out separately and used for counters. Next make a cardboard top, as shown on the right, and push a used matchstick through the centre to make it spin. One player chooses the track marked L, and the other the track marked R. Each places his counter on the correct green footprint at the start. Take turns to spin the top. The number which rests on the table tells you how far you may move. Sooner or later one of you will land on the green footprint of your track. If the other player's next turn takes his counter on to the other green footprint, he has made a "pair" and so wins the game.

RUPERT'S SPRING CHICK

HOLE 'A'

← GUM WHITE PART TO BACK OF SHELL

HOLE 'B' → GUM CHICK'S HEAD HERE ↗

CHICK'S HEAD GUMMED TO BACK OF SHELL

PIPE CLEANER FIXED IN HOLE AND BENT OVER

HOW TO TRACE THE PIECES

This working toy is easy to make. First trace the shape of the baby chick and the top half of the egg, shown above. This can be done by placing a piece of thin card under this page and drawing round the shapes with a firm pencil line. You will find that the lines will appear faintly on the card underneath and they should show clearly enough for you to cut out the card shapes. Next paint your pieces, copying the colours shown in the picture.

HOLE 'C'

CUT ALONG DOTTED LINE

HOW TO MAKE YOUR TOY WORK

Make small holes where shown, one in the chick and one in each part of the egg. Then cut a slot along the dotted line on the lower part of the shell. Your toy is now ready for putting together. Gum the chick's head to the top half of the egg, as in the small drawing. Then slide the chick's body into the slot and push it down until it is hidden from view and the egg is closed. When you do this the two holes 'B' and 'C' of the egg will meet and they should be fastened in place with a short piece of string piece passed through the holes and knotted at the back and front of the card. Turn the page over and fix a pipe cleaner (or a length of stiff wire) in the hole 'A' near the chick's tail. At the top of this page you can see Rupert working the toy—simply give the pipe cleaner a gentle upward push and the chick will pop up from the egg.

RUPERT'S MONKEY PUZZLE

AFTER one of his voyages, Sailor Sam brings home some little monkeys and gives one each to Rupert, Bill Badger, Podgy Pig, Algy Pug and Edward Trunk.

The five pals tie very long strings to their pets and then meet in the wood to let them play.

One of the monkeys immediately runs away, but the other four, delighted to have so much freedom, dash round and round happily until the strings are in a wonderful tangle.

Can you see which of the pals has lost his monkey?

RUPERT'S WINDMILL PUZZLE

"What an odd windmill, Algy," says Rupert. "Let's find out why its sails are star-shaped." They visit the miller, who tells them it is a puzzle for his customers. He shows the pals some coloured shapes, like those round the border of this picture. "See if you can arrange them in the shape of my windmill star," he laughs. "But remember—where the pieces meet the colours must match." To make this puzzle, trace the border pieces and copy the colours. Paste your copies on thin card cut to the same size. Next, study the windmill sails for a few minutes and then put the book aside while you try to make the same star with your puzzle pieces.

RUPERT'S GARDEN COLOURING PICTURE

The big picture is ready for you to paint, and the four small ones, which are exactly the same picture, show you where to put your colours. Start the colouring of the big picture by putting on the tones of red shown in the first small one. Then add the green shades as in the second small picture, and so on until you have put in the blue and yellow as well. Be sure to rinse your brush for each different colour. When you have finished, your big picture will look very pretty.

"REPAIR THE MILL" PUZZLE AND GAME

First try the puzzle. The pictures on the green background are things needed to repair the mill. Arranged in the middle are six different tools, one for each picture. Can you tell which goes with which? To play the game, make a spinning wheel with six sides, as shown in the diagram. Make a hole in the centre of the wheel and push a stump of pencil through it. The two players are allowed to choose three squares each. One player might choose cement, nails and bricks, another might choose screws, glass and wood. Take turns to spin the wheel, which is shaped in such a way that one of its names will lie on the table when it stops. If this name is one of the squares that the player has chosen, then he scores a point. Otherwise he does not score.

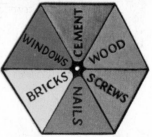

RUPERT'S CROSS-PATH PUZZLE

RUPERT and his friends have set out from Nutwood and are going for a picnic on Robin Down, which they have never visited before. At the edge of Cuckoo Woods they come to an extraordinary crossing where there are no fewer than six signposts!

"What on earth are all these?" gasps Bill. "Ha, ha!" croaks a bird who is watching them. "Those are put there to see how smart people are. Five of the signposts are wrong. Only one of them is correct."

Rupert gazes at them for a moment. Then he leads his pals safely to Robin Down.

Which path does he take? And why?

RUPERT'S FAIRGROUND PUZZLE

"Roll up, roll up and try my giant puzzle!" A jolly-faced clown calls to Rupert and Bill while they are roaming round the summer fair. "What are we supposed to solve?" asks Rupert, staring at the strange puzzle which rests against the wall. "Well, you see those two coloured tabs fixed to the string," says the clown, "they are too large to go through the hole, but can you guess how I managed to get the string through the card without taking the tabs off?" You can have some fun if you make yourself one of these puzzles—you need only some thin card and a piece of string, which are prepared as shown in the blue panel. Then, if you or your chums are unable to solve it, turn to the clown's secret which is given on the back page of this book.

RUPERT

ALGY
and the
SMUGGLERS

Telling how Rupert and Algy when fishing fall into the hands of smugglers. They escape and capture the robber band.

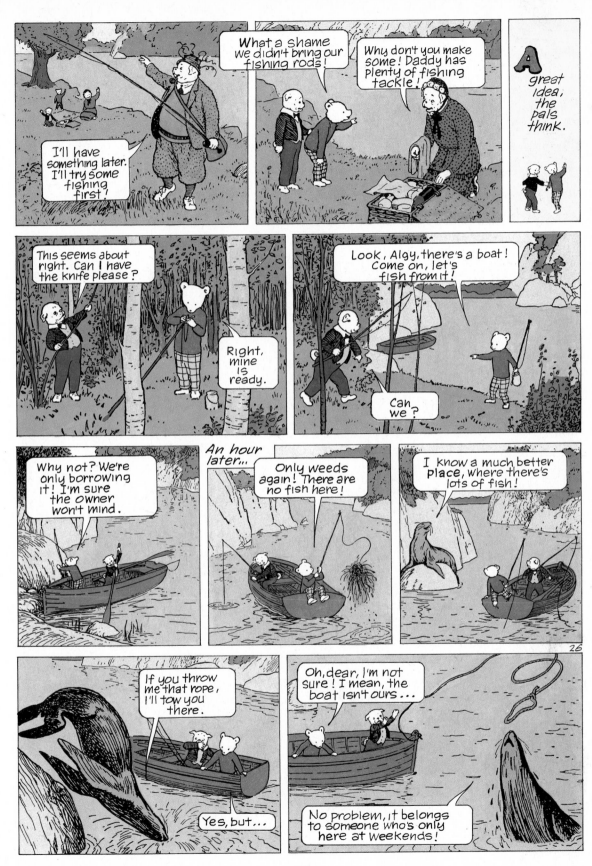

So Rupert and Algy scramble up the rocks as far as they can.

Look at this! A cave! Come on, Algy!

Quick! Here! A chest! What can be in it?

It's half full of parcels... Hello, who are you?

My name is Sylvia! How did you get here?

I'm so glad you're here! You **MUST** help me!

I'm Rupert and he's Algy! Do you live here?

No, but this island belongs to my father. Smugglers have attacked us and locked up my father!

Hush! Somebody's coming!

That'll be the smugglers! Quick, hide!

Algy jumps into the chest as the footsteps come closer and closer...

The chest is too small for the three of us! Hide here!

This thing weighs a lot more than I thought!

Whew! Give us a hand, Pete!

24

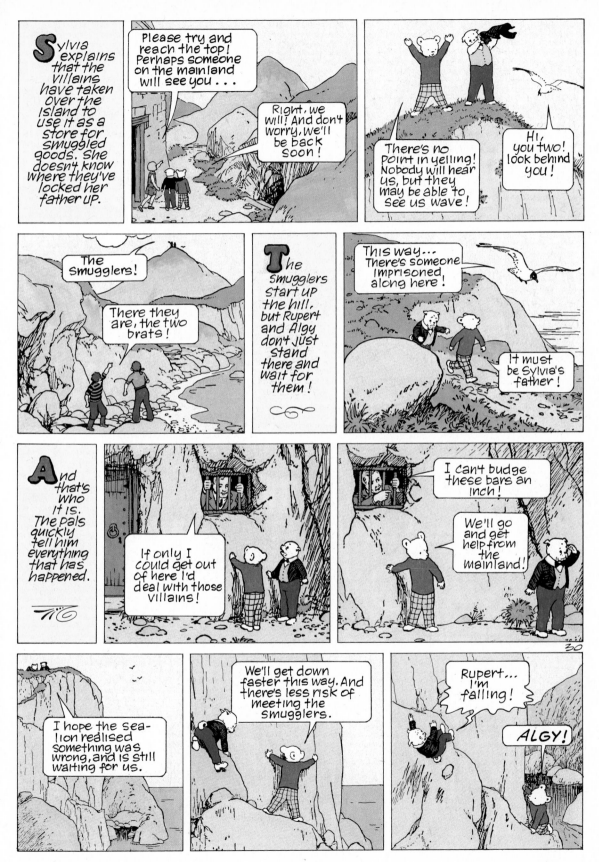

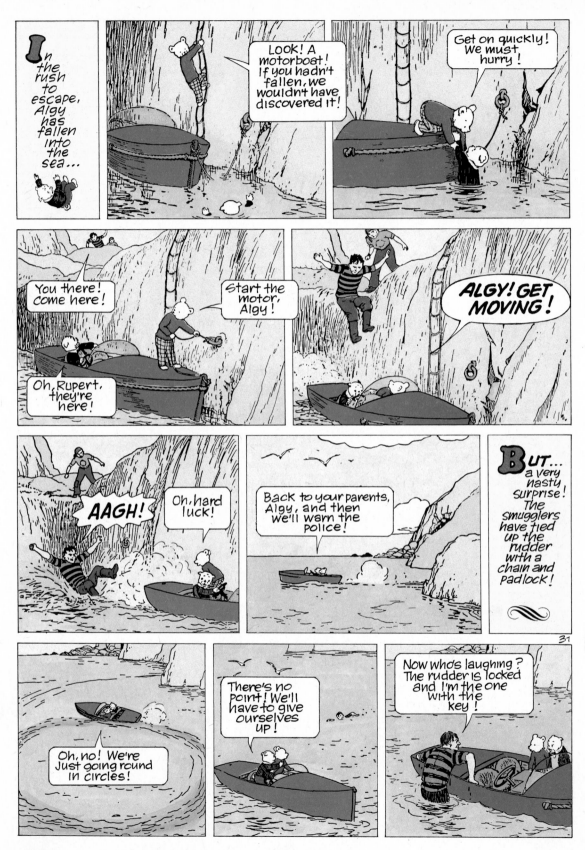

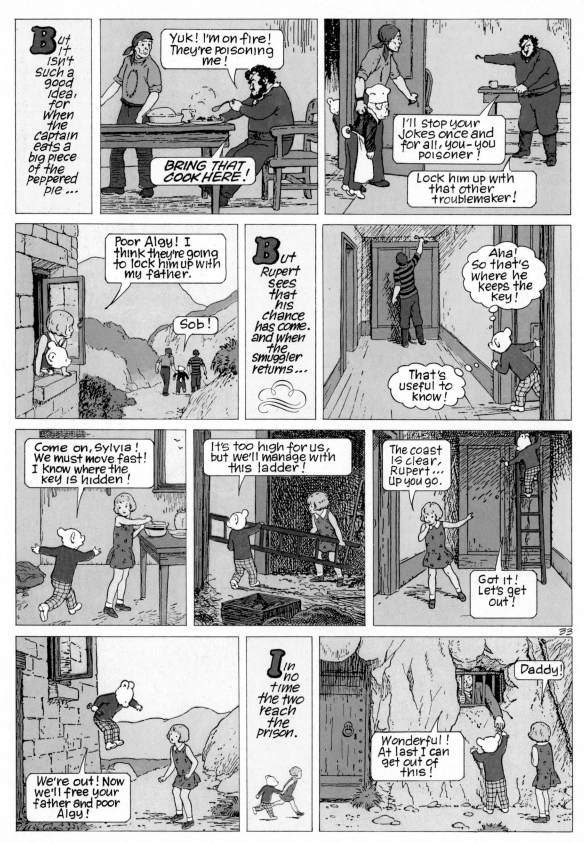

A moment later the door is unlocked and the two prisoners burst out.

Sylvia! Are you all right, darling?

Yes, thanks to Rupert and Algy!

Now I've got a bone to pick with those smugglers...

I've got a few things hidden in here in case of emergency.

What a good idea!

From the hiding place they take a strong rope and a blanket.

First, I'll put you somewhere the smugglers won't find you!

Now I'm going to check the situation. I'll be back as soon as I can.

Can you hold the three of us all at once?

Yes, if I put it around this post, and lower you very slowly!

We better take the blanket inside so they can't spot it from up there!

Look out! I'm coming too!

Sylvia's father arrives, and they all settle down in the cave.

34

29

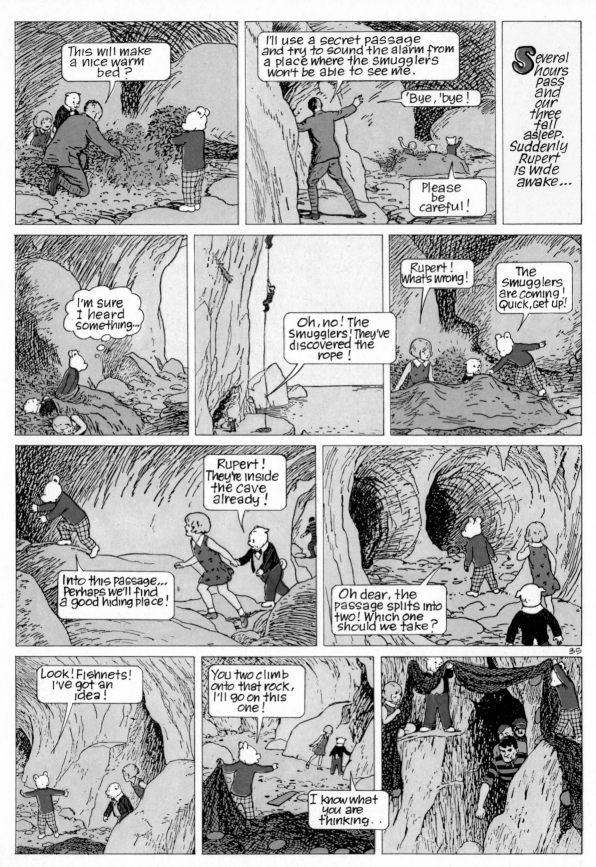

It's worked! We've got them!

That serves you right!

Your father won't believe it, Sylvia!

Let's find Daddy now. Those three won't be able to go anywhere!

If I get my hands on you I'll make mincemeat of you!

Let us out of here at once!

Rupert, Algy and Sylvia take no notice of the threats, and an hour later...

Hello. What happened? I saw your boat floating past and I've been waiting here the whole day!

I'll tell you later. Please, will you swim round the island and look for Sylvia's father?

A little later...

Your daughter and her friends are looking for you!

Coming! I've just undone the chain on the rudder. Are they all right?

Well, I say! I am proud of you!

Oi, watch it will you!

Algy, look! The seagull has found your parents!

What have you been up to, you two? You're not hurt are you?

Mummy! Daddy! We're great! We've caught three smugglers!

We'll deliver these three at the police station. See you soon! Thanks for your help!

'Bye, sir! 'Bye, Sylvia!

We'll come and visit you!

What a pair you are! You go out for a spot of fishing ...

... and come back with three villains in a net!

That night Rupert's Mummy and Daddy want to know if he enjoyed his picnic. He grins. "Enjoyed isn't quite the right word!", he says.

36

31

RUPERT'S ISLAND PUZZLE

"Here's a jolly group of islands," says Sailor Sam. "Let's have a picnic on the distant one with a castle, and we'll make a competition as we go. First we'll all walk down to that red-and-white farm. Then I want you two youngsters to start in opposite directions and see which of you can visit the most islands on your way to the castle. But mind this, neither of you must go to any island twice." "What fun!" cries Bill, "I shall start off to the left of the farm." "Very well," says Rupert, "I'll go to the right."

Which of them can visit the most islands?

And if Sam decides to go by the shortest route, how many islands must he touch?

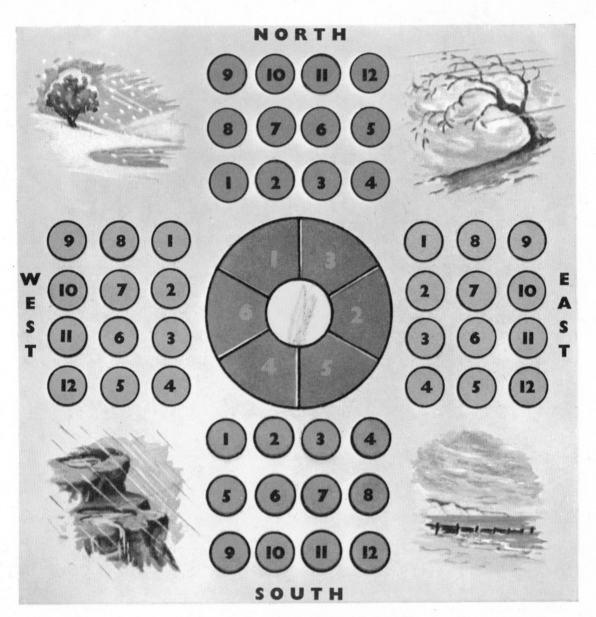

NORTH

WEST

EAST

SOUTH

RUPERT'S "FOUR WINDS" GAME

This game is played with a spinner—look at the foot of the page to see how it is made. Two, three or four players can take part, so choose which of the winds you'd like to be, set the spinner on the yellow centre of the blue circle and your game is ready. Give each player a small counter, which should be placed on the circle marked 1 of the side he has chosen. The players then take turns to spin the arrow (it can be spun by the fingers or blown round). Before a player can start he must score number 6 on the blue circle. After that, any figure which he scores gives the number of circles he can move his counter. For example, if the arrow stops at 4, move the counter four circles, if it stops at 2, move two circles. The game goes on in this manner until one of the players reaches his circle marked 12 and is the winner.

HOW TO MAKE THE SPINNER

On a piece of thin card, draw an arrow the same size as the one on the left, then cut it out and colour it. Now push a pin into the centre dot of the arrow. To stop the arrow slipping down, use a piece of a drinking-straw (about ¼ inch long). Fix the pin into a piece of cork or wood to hold it firmly upright.

33

A PICTURE FOR YOU TO COLOUR

Pong-Ping has made his garden very gay in readiness for the party and he shows Rupert some of the beautiful potted plants which decorate the lawns and paths.

"What a lovely painting your garden would make!" exclaims the little bear. You will think so too when you have coloured this picture of Pong-Ping's garden and his Chinese house.

The small panels down the side are parts of the same picture which has been coloured and cut up. The blue lines on the centre picture show you where the cuts have been made. Compare the coloured panels with the black-and-white picture and you will soon find the matching pieces. Take your paints or crayons and fill in each of the six black-and-white sections in turn, using the coloured panels as your guide. Copy the colours carefully and your finished picture will look very pretty.

RUPERT'S TIDYING-UP MAZE

It is Rupert's busy morning for he is helping his mummy with the housework. One of his jobs is to tidy-up the things which are scattered around, and to put them in their proper places. In the picture are some of the objects he finds and his next task is to decide which goes with which. For instance, the brush and comb go together, and the others also match up one with another. See if you can link each object with its partner by tracing your way through the maze. First choose two objects and, starting at one of them, make your way along the paths until you reach the other. There are twelve objects in all, so you will have to go through the maze five times to complete the puzzle. You may use the same paths more than once, but you must not cross any of the black lines which bar some of the ways. Each time you find two matching objects write down their names and at the end check your answers with those on the back page.

RUPERT'S "WRITE A LETTER" GAME

First write some short messages each on a separate piece of paper and give one to each player. It is important that each message should be different and yet have the same number of letters in it, say fifteen. The idea of the game is to see which player can first cross out all the letters of his message. To do this the players take turns to shut their eyes and put the point of a pencil on the checkered squares of the game. If the pencil lands on a picture, the player must say what the object is. For example, "D" for Dog. If "D" appears on the player's paper it can be crossed off the message. Should the pencil land on a blank square, the player loses his turn. Sometimes a player will be lucky enough to land on one of the squares which contain an alphabet letter. The games goes on in this way until one player has all the letters of his message crossed out. Here are some ready-made messages which you can use to start the game.

PLEASE COME TO TEA.
DO YOU LIKE MY TOYS?
MEET YOU TOMORROW.
I HAVE SOME SWEETS.

THE NUTWOOD CHUMS' KITE PUZZLE

Five chums are flying kites on Nutwood Common. Suddenly they agree to change kites, but in doing so the strings become tangled. Can you find out who is holding which kite? Start at each kite in turn and use a pencil to trace your way along until you reach the chum holding the end of the string. Another part of the puzzle is to name the pals, and you will find the jumbled letters of their names on the kites. When you have your answers, check them with the solution on the back page of this book.

RUPERT

in the
FLOODS

An adventure in deep waters where, with the help of Bill Badger, Rupert saves Podgy from drowning.

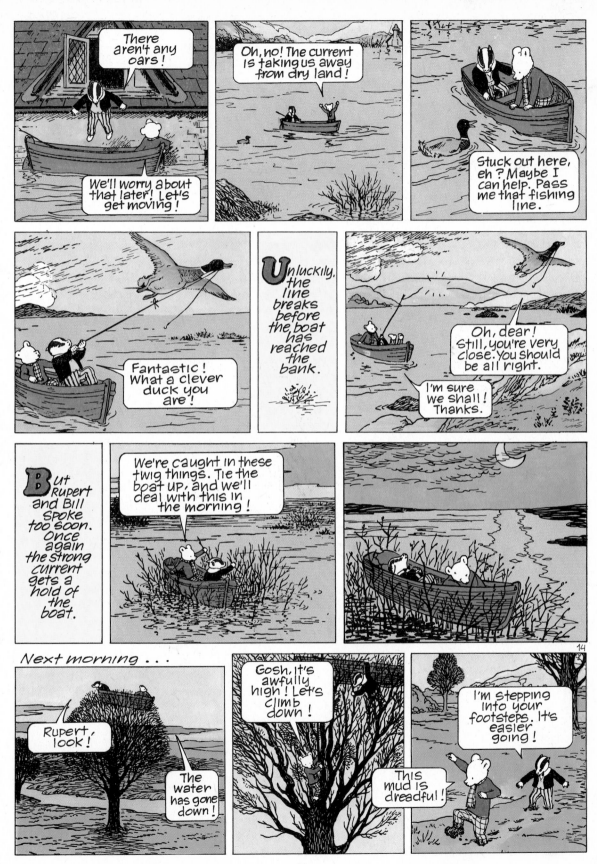

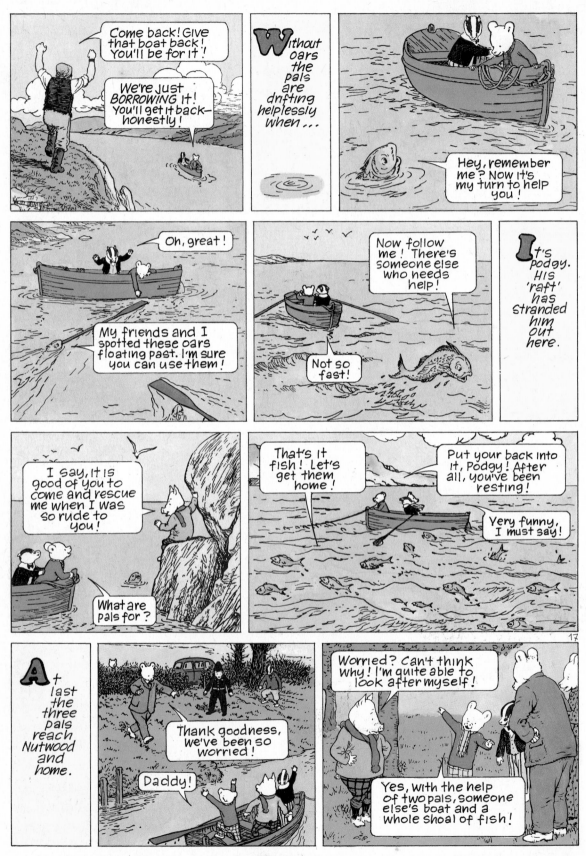